KU-687-690

THE PARENT AND CHILD PROGRAMME

Here Comes Teddy

Jane Salt

Illustrated by Nigel McMullen

Series editor **Penni Cotton**
Senior Lecturer, Reading and Language Studies
Kingston Polytechnic

To Parents

By sharing books together at home you can play a vital part in helping your child learn to read. This series is designed to give the right support to your child in the early stages of reading — so that you can read together with confidence and enjoyment.

How to read this book together

▷ Make reading together a comfortable and special time.

▷ Introduce the story by talking about the characters on page 5. Perhaps your child will have met them in other books in the *Parent and Child Programme*.

▷ **You, as the Storyteller, read the words at the bottom of the page marked with this symbol.**

▷ **After you have read your part, ask your child to join in with the words in the speech bubbles**. All these bubble words are repeated from the words you have just read.

▷ Point to the words in the bubbles as they are read.

▷ On the first reading you could read the story and the first few bubbles yourself so your child thoroughly understands the idea before joining in.

Remember young children love repetition — and the more they read a story the more confident they will feel about joining in or reading their words alone.

Always use the pictures as they give lots of clues. Talk about what the characters are doing and encourage your child to predict what is going to happen next.

If your child is stuck just give the word yourself. This is far more helpful than sounding out individual letters.

Always praise good guesses — much of the skill in reading is in guessing or predicting what the word will be.

Always end reading together on a positive note.

The first day Maria went
to school …

Teddy felt a bit lonely.

So he set off to find her.
"Here I come," shouted Teddy.

He climbed carefully down
the blankets.

8

"Here I come," shouted Teddy.

He drove across the bedroom in Maria's truck.

10

"Here I come," shouted Teddy.

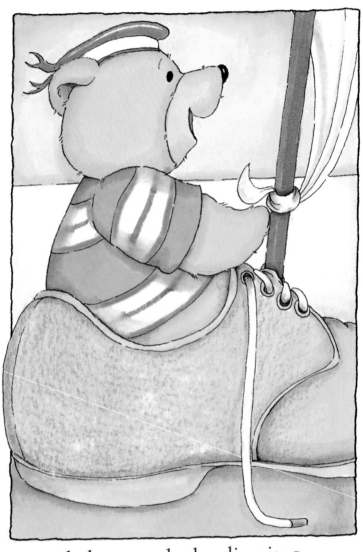

He sailed across the landing in a
big shoe.

"Here I come," shouted Teddy.

He slid down the stairs on a tray.
Bump! Bump! Bump!

14

"Here I come," shouted Teddy.

He rolled down the hall on a
roller skate…

… and bumped into Maria's Mum.
Bang!

"Poor Teddy," said Maria's Mum.
"Are you feeling lonely? Shall I pop
you in my pocket…

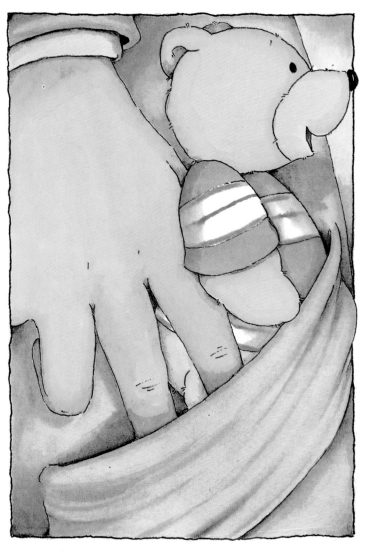

…and take you to find Maria?"
She popped Teddy in her pocket…

...and took him to find Maria.

"Here I come," shouted Teddy.

Outside school, Teddy met his friend
Big Bear

...and they had a little chat.

Then the school door opened
and...

… Teddy jumped right out of Mum's pocket and …

…Maria caught him round his middle.

"Hello Teddy!" she said.

The next day, Maria went to
school again…

... but Teddy didn't feel lonely
because ...

…Big Bear came to play and, anyway, Teddy knew Maria would be home again soon.